Keep Chopping Wood
an ordinary approach to achieving extraordinary success

By Kevin DeShazo

To my wife, Megan, who encourages me, believes in me, cheers me on, puts up with me. You are the greatest gift I have ever known.

To my friends, my community, to those who believed not only only in this project but in me, I am grateful beyond words.

To my boys Gabe, Noah and Asher, everything is for you. You drive me, you inspire me, you make me want to be better. Nothing is better than being Dad to you three.

| Contents

DAY ONE

It was 5:45 in the morning, 15 minutes before his alarm would go off, and Ethan was awake. It was time. Finally. Ethan was a sophomore, and it was his first year on the varsity squad for his high school football team. Today was the day spring ball started and he was bursting with excitement. Mom wished him good luck and dad gave him a fist bump as he headed out the door.

Ethan had been a sports fanatic since he was a little boy. From the age of six, he would wake up before everyone else in the house and watch SportsCenter to get all the news and highlights from the previous day in sports. He was always quizzing his mom and dad with stats from the show, and loved to break down big trades and important games. He even ran his dad's fantasy football team.

He played most sports but football was his first love. From hours in the front yard playing catch with his dad, pretending to catch the Super Bowl winning touchdown, to sitting in the stands for Friday Night Lights at the local high school, Ethan was hooked. Rarely would you see him without a football in his hands.

And he'd been waiting for this day. He was ready to prove himself, to show the upperclassmen he had what it took to be great, to show Coach Thompson what he was made of.

Coach Thompson was a legend in the area. He was a star quarterback and state champion in high school, played in but lost the national championship in college, and had a long NFL career. He was known at that level not necessarily for being the best player, but was the kind of teammate everyone wanted around. He worked hard and made others better. He was a "culture keeper" kind of guy. After retiring, he had a lot of options but ultimately knew he wanted to invest in youth, and he could think of no better place to do that than his hometown. He came home, took a job as an assistant coach and math teacher, and got to work. When the head coach moved on to a bigger town, Coach Thompson was promoted to Head Coach.

During the first practice, the coach had them working on basics. Stances and footwork that Ethan had known for what seemed like his whole life. "We haven't done this since 7th grade. I don't get it. This is varsity. Well, it is the first day. Maybe coach just wants to see where we're at."

Day two looked the same. As did day three and day four. The whole first week of practice was about the basics. Frustrated, Ethan's effort started to diminish. "This is not what I thought it would be. We're never going to win games like this," he thought to himself. By week 3, he had begun gossiping to teammates. "Can you believe this? He's acting like we're in middle school."

Before long, he had become a negative influence on the team, and Coach Thompson called him into his office.

"Ethan, I've noticed you don't seem to be buying into what we're doing. I'm seeing a lot of drama and gossip coming from you, which isn't what I expected when I brought you up to varsity. That's not like you. What's going on?"

"Coach, I don't get it. We're out here doing basic stuff. This is not what I thought varsity football would be. I already know these things. When do we start playing football?"

"We start playing football when we're ready. And we're not ready yet. Most teams get too focused on the 'fun' stuff, and it's the basics that take them out. They get complacent and impatient, and try to get to the next level before they're ready."

"Yeah, but coach, it feels like we're never going to get to the next level. I love football but this is some boring stuff."

"I hear you. But greatness is boring. We see the highlights and the trophies, but the daily work is what gets people there. The truth is that progress is a process, Ethan. And it's not always fun. But the process prepares us for tomorrow by focusing on today, on being brilliant in the basics. And it works. You don't have to love it - shoot, I don't always love it. But you have to trust it, even when it's not fun. And that's the choice you have to make. We have a vision of the kind of team we want to be and the things we want to accomplish. To achieve that, we must commit to the process. If you can't be a healthy member of the team, if you can't be all in, then this may not be for you. I'm not trying to be a jerk about that, but we have a standard. And we all have to be on the same page about the process and live the standard - myself included. When I moved back here, I could've demanded that I be the head coach. Look at my career, what I've done. I could've come in with ego based on what I knew and had accomplished but I knew that wasn't the right way. I've tried that way before and nothing good comes from it. So I came in as an assistant and learned from Coach Jenkins. I learned his process, submitted to his leadership. Had I not done it that way, I probably wouldn't be here today. And it was tough, I'm not going to lie. There were days I didn't want to do it.

But I had to have humility and trust. And that's what you'll need as well. How about this? We're off for the next three days for this break and then we have the weekend. And rest gives us renewed energy and perspective. Why don't you take that time to decide if you really want to be a part of the team. If not, we can both move on. No hard feelings. But, listen to me. I think you could be something special, both as a player and a person. I put you on varsity for a reason, and it's not just about your talent. I hope you'll come around."

THE LESSON

For the short break, Ethan loaded up with his family to go spend time with his grandparents at their farm. He always loved spending time with them, but he wasn't in the best of moods on this trip. His grandpa noticed it, as Ethan spent most of the evening either playing games on his phone or watching TV without speaking to anyone in anything but short sentences.

"Why don't you come with me in the morning? I've got to go out and chop some firewood." "Firewood?" Ethan thought. "It's 55 degrees outside." But he knew better than to argue with his grandpa, so he agreed.

First thing in the morning, he loaded up in grandpa's truck and headed out to the woods. "We need to get two truckloads today, Ethan. We should be done by lunch."

This is not the mini vacation Ethan had in mind. Tired and frustrated after an hour of chopping, Ethan finally spoke up. "Grandpa, why are we doing this? Your rack is full of firewood and it's not even cold. And wasn't this supposed to be a relaxing weekend?"

"This wood isn't for today, Ethan. It's for next year," his grandpa said.

"Wait, what? We're not even going to use this today? This is crazy. What are we even doing?"

"We're chopping wood, Ethan."

KEEP CHOPPING WOOD

"Yeah, wood that won't even be used until NEXT YEAR. Why are we doing this TODAY?"

"Right now this wood is wet. It may not feel wet but it is. If we were lucky enough to get it to burn, it would fill the house with smoke and damage the chimney. It would be a mess and potentially dangerous. Wet wood isn't good wood to burn. So we cut it and it sits for nine months, sometimes longer. In that time it dries out and becomes worth burning."

"So all that wood at the house, you're telling me you chopped that up a year ago?"

"That's right. It dried out over the year and was perfect to burn during the winter. If we waited until it was cold to chop wood, we wouldn't be able to stay warm during the winter. But this winter is almost over, so it's time to prepare for next year. I'm not saying it's fun, but that's the process."

"You sound like Coach Thompson. All about work and no fun."

"Well, coach is right. It is about the process. About the work you put into anything. You don't chop wood to use today, you chop wood today so that you can build a good fire tomorrow. Is it fun today? Of course not. But it pays off down the road. That's what you have to remember. It's not about today, it's about what's to come. Most great things take time. We want what we want today, but that's not how anything worthwhile works. You show up each day and you chop the wood. Understand?"

"Sure, Grandpa," said Ethan. He wasn't really sure. He still didn't understand it, but he also wasn't in the mood to argue about it.

The two got quiet as they went back to chopping the wood. In his mind Ethan was silently, somewhat sarcastically, repeating, "Chop the wood today to have fuel for the fire tomorrow."

As he chopped, his mind drifted back to football and the words of his coach. "Greatness is boring. Be brilliant in the basics. Progress is a process. Trust the process." He then realized what his coach had been saying. And what Grandpa was saying. The team was chopping wood today to prepare them for the fire that is the season to come. They had to focus on the work today so that they could execute at a high level in the game. You don't just show up and win, you must do the work ahead of time. If they want to be a certain kind of team and achieve their goals, they have to show up each day and chop wood. With a new perspective and a new mood, he was excited to get back to school to talk to coach.

THE COMMITMENT

Ethan saw Coach Thompson in the hallway during class and asked if they could meet before practice. "It's time to chop wood, coach!" Confused but intrigued, the coach agreed to meet.

"What's on your mind, son? How was your weekend?" asked Coach Thompson.

"Coach, did you know that the wood you use in your fireplace was chopped a year ago? I mean, it wasn't chopped last week or anything. That wood is a year old." "Actually, Ethan, I did know that. My dad taught me that when I was out chopping wood with him as a young boy. I wasn't a fan of it and didn't understand it, but he explained to me what we were doing and why."

"Well, coach. I realized that what we're doing at practice is chopping wood. It may seem boring and basic, it may not make sense to work on those things today, but it's being great at those things that will help us win games. Like you said, we have to be brilliant in the basics. And that means we chop wood today. That way, when the season comes, we have fuel for the fire. We've prepared for the moment. THAT'S what you mean when you say to trust the process. Chop wood today to have fuel for the fire tomorrow."

"You know, I never thought of it that way. But you're right, That's exactly it. We're chopping wood today so we can fuel the fire tomorrow. Huh. I think you just explained it better than I ever have in all my years of coaching. We prepare for the moment so that we can be prepared in the moment. So I take that to mean you're in? You're sticking with it?"

"Are you kidding me? I'm not just in, coach, I'm all in. Let's go chop wood."

As practice started, Ethan got up to address the team. Not usual for a sophomore but Coach Thompson approved it. "Guys, I need to apologize for my negativity the last few weeks. I know I'm only a sophomore, but I came in thinking I knew everything and was a big deal, and that I was above the work. I wanted to prove myself to you but ended up doing the opposite. I realized this weekend that what we're doing is chopping wood. The thing about chopping wood is that you don't chop it for today, you chop wood a year before you need it. So you have fuel for the fire in the winter. That's what we're doing. Working on mastering the basics so we can be great in the games. We can't just show up and be great. We have to do the work today. We're chopping wood today to fuel our fire tomorrow. I get it now. And I'm in. So let's get to chopping."

Keep chopping wood became a mantra for the team that year. Coach Thompson even went and got an axe (with approval from the school, of course) to keep on the sideline and in the weight room during practices. It was a reminder to be brilliant in the basics. To be masters of their craft. To do the work today to prepare them to excel tomorrow. It was an encouragement to each other in the difficult moments, keeping the team connected, accountable and trusting in each other. "Show me your habits and I'll show you your future," was a phrase Coach Thompson used often. Chopping wood was about developing the right habits today to become the kind of team you want to be tomorrow.

Exercise: Habits

What is your vision? Personally or professionally, who are you trying to become or what are you trying to accomplish? Write it down. Now look at your habits. Will they lead you to achieving that vision or are they going to prevent it from happening? To achieve our vision requires dropping old habits and developing new habits.

What habits will you drop? What habits will you develop?

As the season began, the team was focused and prepared. They executed at a high level, constantly reminding each other to keep chopping wood. In each practice, Ethan made it a point to watch the seniors. He became a sponge, soaking up their wisdom and experience. They had been successful and he knew he needed to learn from them. From their movements in practice to their attitude in the weight room, he was like their shadow. Being younger and weaker, he would consistently fall short. "Keep chopping wood," they reminded him. "Your day will come. We were in your shoes once. Trust us, trust the process. The work is worth it." He realized that influence wasn't only about talent, it was about character. Early in the season he wasn't ready to compete, but through his actions and attitude, he became a leader on the team.

Late in the season, his efforts paid off. He wasn't just a quick learner, he put this new knowledge into practice. And that intentional effort affected his ability on the field. He was out-performing upperclassmen, and the coach couldn't keep him on the bench. As the team neared the end of the season and the playoffs, he became a regular contributor.

KEEP CHOPPING WOOD

With 2 minutes left in the championship game, the team found themselves down by 4, with the ball on their own 11 yard line. They were tired. They were anxious. They felt the pressure. Surely they didn't come this far only to lose in the championship game. As they stood in the huddle preparing for the drive, Ethan stepped in. In the playoffs, he had earned the role of being a starting wide receiver and, even as a sophomore, was one of the more respected voices on the team. "Guys, this is when it pays off. This is why we practiced like we did in the spring and the summer. Those practices I complained

about? It was for this moment. This is why we went through the process we did. This is why we chopped wood. This is where we show that we've got fuel for the fire. Let's go!"

The team marched down the field, efficiently and confidently. With 2 seconds left, Ethan found himself open in the back of the end zone, hauling in what would be the game-clinching, championship winning touchdown. The

team was prepared in the moment because they had prepared for the moment.

They held the trophy up at the end of the season, champions - the first in school history. It was the culmination and celebration of their commitment, both to the process and to each other. They were proud of their accomplishment, but they were even more proud of who they had become along the way. They jumped up and down in celebration, yelling, "Chop wood! Chop wood!"

ROUND 2

As spring ball picked up the following season, Ethan again found himself standing in front of the team. This time, though, he wasn't there to apologize. This time he was just sharing the story of chopping wood and how the work today would prepare them for the season. "We're going to need fuel for the fire during the season, and now's the time we prepare it. Now is the time to chop wood."

This was a younger team, though. They had lost a great group of seniors from the previous year, a group that were not only talented football players, but young men with character and camaraderie. Now that was gone. And while the team was trying to work hard in practice, they were struggling a bit. Ethan noticed it, and kept reminding them to chop wood. They weren't having it, and soon the frustration began to boil over.

"Guys!", Ethan yelled. "Get with it! If you want to be great, you have to get it in gear. This is not going to cut it. If you're in, be in but if you're out, then get out. We won a championship without you last year and we'll win it again this year. Either chop wood or leave." Stunned, Coach Thompson stood on the sideline in silence.

After practice, coach called Ethan into his office. "Bud, what was that about?"

"Coach, these guys don't get it. The effort isn't there. The buy-in isn't there. We've gotta show these guys what it takes to be champions. We can't let them hold us back."

"Gotcha. And you thought berating them in front of the team would get them on board?"

"Well, no. I mean. Somebody had to say *something*."

"Ethan, what you did was call them out. You embarrassed them. I'm not saying you're wrong about the situation, but you help people get to the next level by calling them up. By reminding them of the standard and reminding them who they are. Leaders define culture. And you're one of our culture captains."

"A culture what?" Ethan asked.

"A culture captain. You're someone with influence, someone people look to and follow. How you lead impacts others on the team - for better or worse. The younger players follow your lead. We've been talking about chopping wood for a year, right?"

EXERCISE: Influencers

Who are the Culture Captains on your team or in your department? These are the people who may not have a leadership title, but have influence on those around them (in a business setting, you could call them Culture Influencers). They are crucial to your success and your culture. Have you communicated your expectations to them and prepared them to succeed in this role? Meet with each of them individually and as a group to remind them of who they are and how their example impacts the team.

"Yeah, coach."

"Well, it's not all about the work, it's about the relationships as well. That's the foundation of any great team or culture. When we get into the midst of the season, the team has to know you're for them. They have to know I'm for them. The team has to learn to trust each other in order to fight for each other. Otherwise, we'll collapse any time we're in a tough game."

"Coach, this is football. It's not rocket science. I don't see how this makes us better at football."

"Ethan, the football is the easy part. But life, no matter what team you're on, is about people. It's about relationships. People need to know they trust you. They need to know you're not just out for yourself. They have to want to follow you. So you build the relationships, you spend time connecting with the guys, learning about them. Once they know you're for them, you can call them up to a higher standard. They'll know you're not against them, that you're not trying to be a jerk, but that you're actually fighting for them. And those relationships, those bonds, that trust, it pays off in moments of adversity. We don't just win because we're good at football. We win because we're a great *team* that is connected to each other. Teams must be rooted in trust. That's what we had last year. That's what those seniors were so good at last year. That's the opportunity you have to create now. We do the work of chopping wood to be great at football, but we also have to chop the wood to build strong relationships."

"Ah, I get it. That makes sense. I guess I was so frustrated that all I could see was the lack of effort and execution. Last year went so well that I didn't think much about it. I didn't realize the effort the seniors were making to connect with us but, looking back, it's pretty clear now. I can remember moments where they made time to connect."

"Here's the real key to this, Ethan. It's about your mindset. You can't give what you don't possess. So if you come in here negative and stressed, that's going to come out of you. Just like you need to call them up, you need to first call yourself up. I have a routine each morning. I get up, grab a cup of coffee, read and reflect for a few minutes, then I read what I call my Identity Statement. It's a short statement I wrote several years ago to remind me of who I am, what I'm about, what I'm here for. It's not about what I want to accomplish, it's about who I want to be. Otherwise I lose my way. And I know that better inputs lead to better outputs. On days when I get stressed or anxious, I get out my identity statement to get back on track. It's a way of consistently renewing my mind in order to renew my actions. I think it would be wise for you to come up with an identity statement of your own, and use it each day to call yourself up. That way when you come in, whether that's to school or to the locker room, you're in the right mindset."

Ethan loved that idea and, that night, went home to work on his identity statement. Knowing he would lose a piece of paper, he kept it in the Notes app on his phone so that he would always have it nearby.

EXERCISE: Identity

**Do you have a personal identity statement? A few short
sentences to remind yourself who you are, what you're
about, why you're here? Take some time to create one,
and develop the habit of referring to it each day. Make a
practice of calling yourself up to the best version of you.**

The next day before practice, Ethan made it a point to go
sit with some of the younger guys. They joked around and
got some laughs in, then shifted into work mode as they
headed out to the practice field. "Let's have a great day of
practice, fellas," Ethan encouraged. "I believe in you
guys."

Over the course of the season, Ethan intentionally made
time to interact with different groups. Other leaders on the
team followed suit. Rather than always being split up by
position group, offensive players mixed in with defensive
players, upperclassmen connected with underclassmen.
The bonds needed to stick together during adversity were
being formed. The team even created what they called The
Golden Axe Award, and each month the players would

give it to the teammate who best lived out the values and culture of the team. They didn't want all this stuff to just be talk, they wanted it to be put to practice and, when it was, celebrated and rewarded.

EXERCISE: Connection
We live in a results focused world, but we don't get results without people. A connected team is a committed team. How well do you know your team (1-10)? Be honest. How well does the team know each other (1-10)? What will you put into practice to develop deeper relationships and connection with your team? By when?

THE BIGGER PICTURE

A s Ethan's high school career went on, the team would win two more state titles. It was the best run in school history, and each team bought into the mantra of chopping wood. They left a legacy not just of winning, but of winning the right way.

Chopping wood was about more than sports, though, it was about life. As Ethan excelled in sports, he would struggle a bit in school. It was difficult and, at times, frustrating but Ethan was committed to graduating. Neither of his parents had gone to college, and he wanted to chart the course of a new legacy for his family. Seeing her son struggle, Ethan's mom tried to relieve the pressure. "It's okay, son. We know you're smart. We see how hard you work. All we ask is that you do your best."

"I know, mom. But I have to keep chopping wood. If I want to graduate and get into college, I need the grades. And if I want the grades, I have to pass the classes. And if

I want to pass the classes I have to study. So I'm chopping wood today to prepare for tomorrow."

His mom laughed. "It's always about chopping wood with you, isn't it? Who knew how much one day with grandpa would change things, right?"

"It really did, mom. It changed everything. I may not like the work, I mean, who likes to study? But I know it will pay off in the future."

"I'm proud of you, Ethan. It would've been easy to complain that day. And it would be easy to complain during football practice and while studying for tests. But you've stayed positive. You've kept your head down and done the work. As you say, you've chopped the wood. And that's the most important part. Winning games and passing tests are good things, but I'm more concerned about who you're becoming along the way. You've been fortunate to have good outcomes but the truth is we can't control outcomes. You can't control whether or not you win games or pass tests. But whether you're winning or losing, you can control your attitude and your effort. And you've done that."

Throughout his life, the mantra of chopping wood served Ethan well. Not only did he graduate from high school, he earned a scholarship to college, becoming the first person in his family to attend. Walking across the stage, shaking the hand of his Principal while being handed his diploma, knowing how hard he had worked and what he had accomplished, was a day that Ethan would never forget. It wasn't easy, but all of those hours studying had paid off.

As a kid, Ethan loved to draw. His last year of high school, he had been constantly tinkering with a drawing of an axe and a chopped piece of wood. Before heading off to college in the fall, Ethan got a tattoo of the drawing, to be sure to never forget the lessons of chopping wood.

Exercise: Visions

Images and phrases remind us of our vision, of who we're trying to be and what we're trying to accomplish. What phrases does your team use? Are they just phrases or are they being lived out? What can you do to make those more visible, as constant reminders of the vision? What can you do to celebrate when you see people living those standards?

THE STRUGGLE

I t was the fall semester of his third year in college, finals week, and Ethan was overwhelmed. Late one night, he sat alone in the library with his head in his hands. After slacking for most of the semester, his grades were struggling. He skated for the first two years of school, but this year was different. This was his third straight all-nighter, preparing for a final and he could barely keep his eyes open. If he didn't pass the test, he would fail the class. And if he didn't pass the class, he would lose his scholarship. He was exhausted and the weight of his situation was bearing down on him. "You know what, forget it," he thought to himself. "I don't need this stress. I'll just go get a job. Nobody else in my family even went to college. I'll be fine."

After the test, Ethan only felt worse. He knew he had failed. He knew his scholarship was gone. He spent the next week in a funk, ashamed and embarrassed by his efforts. Quitting looked more appealing than ever. His parents were coming into town for the weekend and he didn't know what to tell them.

His mom had always told him to never be afraid to ask for help, that he didn't have to do it alone. "It's okay to not be okay," she would say. "But it's not okay to not be okay and not ask for help." Embarrassed but remembering her advice, Ethan was about to pick up the phone to call her when he looked down at his wrist. He'd seen the tattoo a million times at this point, mostly ignoring it. But this time was different. This time he saw the tattoo and, in his mind, was immediately back in the woods with his grandpa - who had passed away earlier this year. *Chop wood today to have fuel for the fire tomorrow.* He also heard his mom's words, reminding them that win or lose, he controls his attitude and effort. He realized he hadn't been living that lesson this semester. He got complacent. He was more interested in playing video games than studying. He was living accidentally instead of intentionally. His unhealthy habits were pointing to an unhealthy future. And now he was paying the price.

Ethan told his parents the truth that weekend, that he was
going to lose his scholarship. They were disappointed but
also encouraging. "Son, I can't tell you how many times
I've failed. How many wrong decisions I've made. It's part
of life. We don't expect you to be perfect and you can't
expect that of yourself. All you can do is the best you can
do. And if you didn't give your best, be honest with
yourself. And instead of beating yourself up, do the work
to get better. This is just a moment in your story, not the
end of the story. Tell me, do you want to graduate from
college?"

"Of course, dad."

"Okay, great. Do you believe you can graduate from college?"

"Sure. I think so."

"I didn't say do you *think* you can graduate from college, I asked if you believe you can?"

"Yes, dad," Ethan said begrudgingly. "I believe I can."

"Alright, good. There's an obstacle in front of you that you have to overcome. But you can overcome it, if you believe you can. Belief drives behavior. When you get down, remind yourself that you believe in yourself. And that we believe in you. Even say it out loud if you have to. Belief is a powerful force and when we believe, we look for a way forward. When we doubt, we look for a way out."

EXERCISE: Belief

Refer back to your vision statement. Do you believe in it? Do you believe it's possible? And do you believe in yourself? We all have moments of doubt. It's normal. Write down the doubts that are holding you back, and then counter those doubts with statements of belief.

After they left, Ethan felt better about his situation. He was still embarrassed by his effort, but also knew what he was capable of. He knew that he hadn't given his best. He re-committed that weekend to continuing, to growing, to finishing. He was committed to doing the work required to graduate, even without his scholarship. He was committing to getting back to chopping wood.

WOOD CHOPPING 101

After graduation, Ethan got a job at a tech start-up in Texas. Excited about the opportunity and wanting to make a good impression, Ethan hit the ground running. With it being a small company, he was doing sales, customer service, marketing and a bit of administrative work. It was a lot, but it was also exciting. He asked questions and took notes, studying from the leaders in the company. It took a few months for him to get up to speed, but he had put a picture on his desk of him and his grandpa, with the phrase, "Keep chopping wood." He knew the work he put in today would make him a great asset to the company, no matter the role. He stayed positive, he trusted in the process the company had in place, and he committed to the work.

Eight months in, Ethan had found his way. He became the fastest person in company history to earn a promotion, and he became known for his catchphrase he would say as he left each day. "Great day of chopping wood, friends! Back at it tomorrow." Nobody knew what it meant, but they knew that whatever it was, it was working. Ethan was unstoppable and his optimism was infectious. While he was pretty good at everything he did, he (and the company) discovered he had a natural knack for sales. One co-worker stopped him in the break room one day, "Ethan, I have to ask. I mean, you're killing it out there. Even when you do have a down month, you bounce right back. What's your secret?"

"I'm just chopping wood, Tiffany. To be honest, I don't focus on the results, I try to focus on doing the work each day. And you're right. I do have down days or sometimes a down month. We all do. I do what I can to not let that bad month turn into a bad quarter, which could turn into a bad year. I try to learn what caused it, change what I can change and keep doing the work."

Not only was Ethan great with clients, he also loved helping others on the team get better. He would share lessons he'd learned from his successes and his failures to help others grow. Soon, he found himself as the lead sales trainer. He was so effective that they wanted him to teach all the new hires how to be successful in sales. Ethan wasn't prideful, but he knew his system worked. He also knew the only way to make it a win for the entire company was to teach it to others. He had to multiply the magic in his head to the rest of the sales staff, equipping them for success. He was thrilled by the opportunity to invest in the team in this way.

Ethan called his training, no surprise, "Wood Chopping 101." He would preach the basics to the new, hungry sales staff. "This may not seem exciting, and it may seem simple, but if you become brilliant in the basics you'll find success. It's a proven process. Trust in it, commit to it, believe in yourself. The results will come if you keep chopping wood. And remember you're not alone. We're all in this together."

Exercise: Multiply
Who are the people on your team who are the best in a certain area? How can you equip and empower them to multiply their magic to others, in order to increase the skill level of everyone on the team?

39

Ethan also knew that if the company truly wanted to be great, it was about more than sales numbers. He remembered the lessons of Coach Thompson back in high school, that it's not just about being great at the job, it's about being a great team. One day he asked his boss Sarah, one of the Senior VPs, if he could lead a team building session. "Team building session? Ethan, I don't know if you've noticed, but we're flying high right now. We just had our best quarter ever - thanks to your sales training. What do you call it, Wood Chopping class? Everyone seems to love that. Anyway, I think our team is pretty good."

"You're right, Sarah. We are. We're killing it right now, no question. And that's a credit to you and your leadership. But adversity always hits. And we'll need more than just our sales skills to get us through. I used to have this football coach, Coach Thompson. Best leader I've ever known. One day in practice I was getting upset about the lack of effort from the underclassmen and I went off on them. I called them out and embarrassed them. Coach Thompson reminded me that great teams are about relationships and trust. That instead of calling people out, I needed to call them up. He said that at some point our team would face an obstacle, and how connected we were as a team would be what caused us to either overcome that obstacle or be overcome by the obstacle. I think the same is true for us. What I've realized is that we don't really know each other. Our numbers are good but there's no real trust or connection. When I first started and was involved in several departments, I remember how marketing and sales felt like they were competing instead of collaborating. The customer service team felt left out and the administrative staff were always talked down to. Everyone is doing their job well, but it's mostly because it's a paycheck. Sure we have fun but that's because we're winning. Winning tends to hide issues. But if we can connect as a team and build real trust, we can be something special. Instead of operating in silos, we can come together and lean on everyone's strengths. We can build a legacy of success and a culture that will get us through the tough times. But it won't happen by accident. As leaders, we define culture. They're following us. If we want it from the team, we have to live it ourselves. I think

I can teach the whole company what it means to chop wood today so that we have fuel for the fire tomorrow, and it's about more than sales. It's about the people. I think the things we are experiencing are pretty normal. And the way we operate, for the most part, is pretty normal. As I talk to friends in others organizations I'm hearing a lot of similar issues. But normal isn't who we are. I say instead of settling for normal, we go for greatness. "

"I can't really argue with that, Ethan. And you've definitely earned the benefit of the doubt. Let's set it up."

A few months later, Ethan stood up in front of the company. When he started, only 25 people worked for the company. Now they were up to 100 employees. Here he was in front of all of them, talking about wandering in the woods with his grandpa.

"Did you know that you chop firewood a year before you need it?" he asked the team. He went on to share the lesson his grandpa had taught him, about how that lesson changed his attitude in high school and changed the entire team. He told them about coach Thompson and becoming valedictorian. He told them about almost quitting in college, about failing, about the tattoo and about pressing on. "To be honest, guys, I'm here today because I just keep chopping wood. And every time there's an opportunity in front of me, every time there's a need for a fire, I'm ready. And I've failed plenty of times. I've had down months, but I keep doing the work. But it's about more than just being great salespeople or great at marketing or great customer service reps. It's about being a great team. And we have great people in every area. I remember our early days when I spent time in what seemed like every department. Marketing, I know how you feel. Customer Service, your work isn't glamorous but it's so important and you guys are terrific. Our amazing administrative staff, you don't get enough attention but you are rock stars. IT, you keep this whole thing up and running. Sales, we may feel like rock stars but nothing happens without all of us working together. Because at some point we're going to face adversity. We're going to have to pick each other up, fight for each other, link arms together as we try to move forward. There's going to be a fire that needs tending to. And if we don't do the work now, we won't be ready. Over the next few months we're going to start working on some things to make us more connected. We're going to work on chopping wood together. We're going to build our relationships, work on our communication, build real trust. I know it sounds cheesy and some of you are probably questioning what in the world I'm talking about. That's okay. I felt the same way when Coach Thompson said it to me. But I had to have humility and trust. And so will you. Because here's what I know. When we come together as a team, when we learn to chop wood together, we'll be unstoppable."

Over the next few months, Ethan started doing more than sales training, he started doing culture training. He would mix up teams of employees from every department to build relationships across department lines. He helped people learn to understand themselves and their tendencies. He helped uncover communication styles, strengths and weaknesses. He helped them see how when they played to their strengths and empowered others to do the same, everyone rises. He got them to understand that no department is working against another department, but instead we're all working together to support each other. Beyond that, he helped them understand each other's stories. He knew that if they could see beyond job titles and descriptions, they would build real connections and learn to fight for each other. This would be the real benefit of chopping wood together. Ethan even brought back The Golden Axe Award from his high school days, to celebrate and acknowledge the team member each month who best lived out the values and culture of the company. He knew that to change behaviors, to get rid of culture killing behaviors they had to start celebrating and rewarding behaviors that built the right culture.

EXERCISE: Behaviors
There are culture killers and culture builders on your team. These aren't people, but behaviors. List out the culture killers (insecurity, ego, isolation, etc). Then list out culture builders (communication, humility, collaboration, etc). How will you celebrate culture building behaviors and work to eliminate culture killing behaviors?

FUEL FOR THE FIRE

A year later the economy started to struggle. Their industry appeared to be on shaky ground and there was a nervousness around the office. Sarah was now the CEO and had asked Ethan, now a Senior VP of Culture, to speak at their company retreat. It was a critical moment for the company and Ethan knew it. He stood up and reminded them of who they were and the work they had done. "We knew this day would come. Nothing great ever comes without adversity. We're great people who have been doing great work, and our obstacle is here. Will we overcome it or will we be undone by it? All of those meetings, all of those conversations, all of those sessions we've been doing. All that wood we chopped? It was for a moment like this. A year ago, I believe this kind of adversity would've taken us out. We would've turned inward, gotten negative and territorial and our company would've crumbled. But, thanks to Sarah's leadership and your efforts, we're not today who we were yesterday. We've chopped wood together. I believe in you all and what we're capable of. Let's stick together, let's be who we are."

Sure enough, the company made it through. It was a difficult year. They had to adjust expectations, they had to truly trust each other and they had to maintain their level of belief, but they made it. While success looked different than it did in previous years, they were the only business in their industry to not lay anybody off - several competitors folded completely. "Success looks different at different times," Sarah told them. "Sometimes it looks like growth, sometimes it looks like not going backwards. We know this year hasn't been easy. What we've done this year is worth celebrating. Thank you to Ethan for leading these efforts but also to you all for buying in and committing to getting better. We can communicate culture from the top but it's built from the bottom. You all had a choice to make, to be in or to be out. You decided to be in and you've been all in. It's humbling to work and run alongside you all. We don't have a leadership team, we have a company full of leaders at every level."

Ethan knew that chopping wood was about more than work, though. It was about life. He knew he had to be as great at home as he was at work. "None of this matters if

I'm not living it at home. I don't want everyone talking at my funeral to be from work, talking about the impact I made, with my wife and kids sitting in the pew wondering who in the world everyone is talking about, wishing they'd had that version of me."

And Ethan was intentional at home. He told his wife Rachel about the principle of chopping wood while they were dating and, while she laughed at how corny it was, it became part of the language of they used around investing in each other and the family. From date nights with his wife to game nights with the family to coaching his kids sports teams and helping with homework. One of the things they wanted to create as parents - at least as best as they could - was open communication with their kids. Like great teams, they believed great families ran on trust. They wanted their kids to know that they were always available for them, always a resource, always willing to listen. So each night at bedtime, Ethan and Rachel would sit at the end of their kids' beds and just chat. Nothing specific, no agenda, just a way to wind down the day together. They realized that this setting tended to lead to more open conversations, to questions about life, to hearing about what was "really" going on. It was the time of day where their kids were more willing to process. For Ethan and Rachel, this was their way of planting seeds of trust, presence and connection, and as time went on this became one of their favorite moments of the day, for both the parents and the kids.

They had a vision for their family as a unit and for their children, and they knew those wouldn't come to life on accident. They were intentional in building the relationships, in having certain conversations, and even developed an apprenticeship plan to use with their kids once they hit their teenage years.

Exercise: A lifestyle
Leadership isn't just about your job, it's about life. If you have a family, how intentional are you in being present, connecting and leading well (1-10)? Does your family get the best version

of you or are they getting your leftovers? What will you do to increase your level of intentionality with your family? (if you don't have a spouse and/or kids, use your friendships here)

The years would go on and Ethan continued to share the chopping wood concept with his team and organization, his family and his friends. He couldn't believe the impact that one lesson in the woods with his grandpa would have, not only on his life but on those around him. Over coffee with a friend one day, the topic came up - as it always did. "I guess I'll just always be known as the chopping wood guy. And you know what? That's perfectly okay with me. I'll take that as I've made an impact."

One day Ethan's oldest daughter Emily, a freshman on the basketball team, came home frustrated. She wasn't on the same page as the coach and felt frustrated with the team as a whole. "Nobody gets it, dad. I don't even know if I want to play if it's going to be like this." Ethan smiled. His wife, overhearing the conversation, smiled. A long weekend was ahead. Ethan got up the next morning, made breakfast for him and his daughter and loaded up the truck.

"Emily, have I ever told you about your great grandpa? Boy, he could chop some wood."

Keep Chopping Wood

The lessons in this book are simple but, I believe, practical and powerful. It's not just a concept to think about, but a practice to live out. We live in a world that wants immediate results. A world where you can drive thru to get your food, your clothes, your money, your medicine. But when it comes to building a great team or business, or even learning a new skill, there is no drive thru. It takes time. It's a process. And instead of looking for a shortcut or lifehack, the best know that you show up each day. If you want to achieve your goals, you must do the work. You sacrifice and commit today so that you can enjoy the fruit of your efforts tomorrow.

You save money today so you can retire (or go on vacation) tomorrow.
You eat well and work out today so you'll be healthy and alive tomorrow.
You run the short miles today so you can run the marathon tomorrow.

KEEP CHOPPING WOOD

You write the words today so they will be a book tomorrow.

You practice the shots today so you can make it in the game tomorrow.

You study today so you can graduate tomorrow.

You invest in your people today so you can be a great team tomorrow.

Chopping wood is about dedication, about patience, about trust, about belief. It's having a vision for who and where you want to be, a game plan to get there, and the discipline to do the work each day. It's about developing the habits that help you become the kind of person you were meant to be. Ultimately, it's about rejecting mediocrity and pursuing greatness. And you were made for greatness.

Wherever you are on your path, remember where you are going and remember why you started. And keep chopping wood.

ACKNOWLEDGEMENTS

A massive thank you goes out to those who have supported this project, but especially the launch team. They've given feedback, shared the message with their network and been an incredible support system. A special thanks to Andy Schoggin for helping to come up with the subtitle, to Trey Jackson for his design work and for Eric Silvestri for his illustration skills.

Jim Powers	Kwynten Gage	Sallie Guillory	Loren
Nicholas Herrington	Derick Stoulil	Kelly Mosier	Thomas Pool
Rob Simmerman	Brenadan Heitz	Michael Trotter	Andy Guyon
Stephanie Dutton	Matt Vincent	Andy Carter	Mike Odom
David Wiechmann	Zach Dayton	Fred Smith	Mike Snyder
Mark Hodgkin	Justin Gordon	Lonnie Hill	JP Abercrumbie
Tom Buchheim	Ian Sadler	Kevin Richardson	Chris Yandle
Eric Scott	Tyler Pigg	Suzi Lantz	Jeremy Bussell
Konner Beste	Tod Meisner	Kelly Bommer	Cade Smith
Susan DeWoody	Andy Harris	Evan Dare	Greg Bamberger
Katie Gates	Cassie Gage	Andy Schoggin	Jerry Lawrence
Jeremy Capo	Nathan Werremeyer	Josh Remington	Karl Mealor
Beth Brown	Blake Timm	April Cole	Robert Sampson
Adam Klatskin	Tim Collins	Jay Fletcher	Jamie Mitchell
Will Brantley	Dennan Morrow	Patrick Schulte	Joe Reinsch
Brent Nolan	Nick Schmidt	David Brock	Katie Cavender
Gary Paczesny	Austin Schindel	Sam Knehans	Chris King
Paul Thomas	Danny Kambel	Chris Rammel	Steven Riddle
Adam Schemm	Ryan Holmes	Jeff Mitchell	Tanner Lipsett
Dan Montano	Robbie Britt	Taryn Carrol	BJ Merriam
Jamie Bartlett	Jerome Learman	Eric Hehman	Morgan Romas
Natasha Brophy	Scott Dempsey	Kevin Bille	Chris Forman
Steve Thompson	Terry Mangan	Ryan Gaines	Zack Lassiter
Nick Moen	Drew McCarty	Joe Skinner	Josh Dunst
Cullen Dees	Genese Lavalais	MK	Lynn Coutts
Alyssa Murphy	Scott Martin	Emily Punt	Bryson Rosser

KEEP CHOPPING WOOD

Jessica Rhodes	Mike Grasta	Brooke Porter	Terry Saul
Jonny Dierks	Jeffrey Epperly	Angie Jabir	Kendall Mayer
Jermie Howell	Matt Thorne	Michael Meshaw	Scott Peace
Chris Mycoskie	Garret Griffeth	Leon Friedrich	Michael Mitchell
Scott Day	Kristie Beitz	Ben Dignan	Emily Dorko
Rob Carolla	Brad Hall	Zac Workun	John Roy
Melinda Brenton	Ryan Kumpf	Matt Vaughan	Jacob Weaver
Angel Webster	Teddy Owens	Adam Ledyard	Jessica Lee
Brady Fritz	Traci Runge	Giancarlo Lemmi	Casey Cariker
Brenda Viator	Kaleena Schumacher	Mark Herringshaw	Spencer Ferrari-Wood
Gabriel Achayo	Kristia Worthy	Bill Gamble	Brian Wagner
Ken Surritte	Ryan Keirn	Justin Morris	Jessica Rimmer
Chris Dunning	Patrick Myers	Sam Ferguson	Mikel Hartman
Kaycee Tripp	Scott Grant	Patti McGowan	Tyler Carlton
Michael Taylor	Ryan Wellner	Dillon Stanley	Kyle Sheldon
Megan Hinners	Henry Barrera	Ryan MacTaggart	Nate Thiry
Owen Field	Jonathan Howard	Tyler Swope	Ben Coldagelli
Joseph Colletti	Lindsey Bryan	Lisa Rossi	Julie Powell
Brigette Zorn	Steven Flowers	Connelly Rader	Leslie Schuemann
Doug Self	Jose Larios	Chris Grant	

ABOUT THE AUTHOR

As the founder of Fieldhouse Media and a partner at Culture Wins (the sports division of global leadership development firm GiANT), Kevin DeShazo works with some of the best leaders, teams and organizations in the industry of sports.

A sought after keynote speaker, he has presented on more than 250 college campuses and headlined top sports conferences and conventions.

He has appeared in Sports Illustrated, ESPN.com, The New York Times, Bleacher Report, USA Today and a number of other national and local media platforms. He has written two previous books, *iAthlete: impacting student-athletes of a digital generation* and the Amazon best-seller *Leadership Interrupted: daily inspiration to become the leader you were meant to be.*

He calls Oklahoma City home, along with his wife, Megan, and their three boys, Gabe, Noah and Asher.

To book Kevin for your event, email kevin@deshazo.me, call 405.535.6943 or visit his website at www.deshazo.me

Made in the USA
Las Vegas, NV
09 December 2024

13677932R00038